Other titles in the Overcoming series:

3-part self-help courses

Overcoming Low Self-Esteem Self-Help Course
Overcoming Bulimia Nervosa and Binge-Eating Self-Help Course

Single volume books

Overcoming Anger and Irritability
Overcoming Anorexia Nervosa
Overcoming Anxiety
Bulimia Nervosa and Binge-Eating
Overcoming Childhood Trauma
Overcoming Chronic Fatigue
Overcoming Chronic Pain
Overcoming Compulsive Gambling
Overcoming Depression
Overcoming Insomnia and Sleep Problems
Overcoming Low Self-Esteem
Overcoming Mood Swings
Overcoming Obsessive Compulsive Disorder
Overcoming Panic
Overcoming Relationship Problems
Overcoming Sexual Problems
Overcoming Social Anxiety and Shyness
Overcoming Traumatic Stress
Overcoming Weight Problems
Overcoming Your Smoking Habit

All titles in this series are available by mail order.
Please see the order form at the back of this workbook.

www.overcoming.co.uk

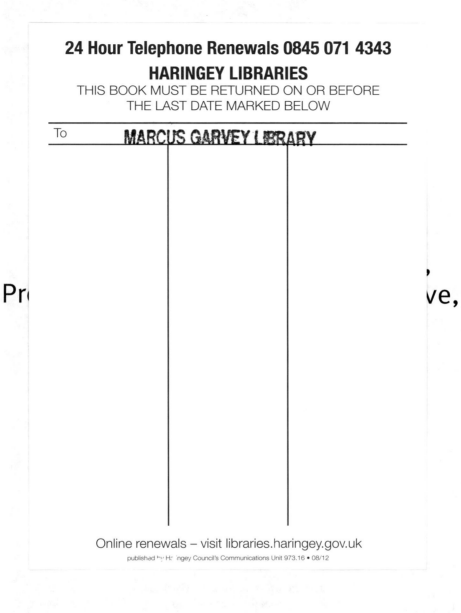

Pr   ve,

ROBINSON
London

Constable & Robinson Ltd
3 The Lanchesters
162 Fulham Palace Road
London W6 9ER
www.overcoming.co.uk

First published in the UK by Robinson,
an imprint of Constable & Robinson Ltd 2006

A copy of the British Library Cataloguing in
Publication Data is available from the British Library.

Important Note
This book is not intended as a substitute for medical advice or treatment.
Any person with a condition requiring medical attention should consult
a qualified medical practitioner or suitable therapist.

ISBN 13: 978-1-84529-235-5 (Pack ISBN)
ISBN 10: 1-84529-235-9

ISBN 13: 978-1-84529-416-8 (Part One)
ISBN 10: 1-84529-416-5

ISBN 13: 978-1-84529-417-5 (Part Two)
ISBN 10: 1-84529-417-3

ISBN 13: 978-1-84529-418-2 (Part Three)
ISBN 10: 1-84529-418-1

1 3 5 7 9 10 8 6 4 2

Printed and bound in the EU

Contents

Introduction   vii

SECTION 1: Managing Avoidance – Graded Practice   1

SECTION 2: Problem-Solving   17

SECTION 3: Being Assertive   29

SECTION 4: Time Management   39

SECTION 5: Getting a Better Night's Sleep   53

SECTION 6: Coping in the Long Term   61

Extra Charts and Worksheets   67

Note to Practitioners

This self-help course is suitable for a wide range of reading abilities and its step-by-step format makes it ideal for working through alone or under supervision. The course is divided into three workbooks, and each contains a full supply of worksheets and charts to be filled in on the page – so there is no need for photocopying. If you do decide to photocopy this material you will need to seek the permission of the publishers to avoid a breach of copyright law.

Introduction: How to Use this Workbook

This is a self-help course for dealing with problem worries, fears and anxieties. It has two aims:

1 To help you develop a better understanding of the problem

2 To teach you some practical coping skills

How the course works

The *Overcoming Anxiety Self-Help Course* will help you understand how anxiety develops and what keeps it going, and then to make changes in your life so that you begin to feel more confident.

These workbooks are designed to help you work, either by yourself or with your healthcare practitioner, to overcome anxiety. With plenty of questionnaires, charts, worksheets and practical exercises, the three parts together make up a structured course.

Part One explained the origins and development of problem worries, fears and anxieties. You learnt:

- What anxiety and stress are

- Whether you have a problem with anxiety

- What the difference is between helpful short-term anxiety and unhelpful long-term anxiety

- Why anxiety has become a problem for you

- The cycles that maintain and worsen your anxiety

- What kind of anxiety disorder you might be suffering from

Part Two explained:

- How to ease the physical sensations of anxiety through controlled breathing and relaxation techniques

- How to deal with worrying thoughts

- How to face your fears using planning and problem-solving

Part Three gives advice on:

- Assertiveness training to help you handle relationships better

- Time management to help you improve decision-making and your organizational skills

- Sleep management to help you get a better night's rest

- Guidance for coping with anxiety in the long term

How long will the course take?

Although it will vary from person to person, it will probably take you at least two or three weeks to work through each workbook. You should not worry if you feel that you need to give certain parts extra time. Some things can be understood or practised quite quickly, but others may take longer. You will know when you are ready to move on to the next workbook. Completing the entire course could take two to three months, or it could take more or less time – it depends how quickly you wish to work.

Getting the most from the course

Here are some tips to help you get the most from the workbooks:

- These workbooks are not priceless antiques – they are practical tools. So feel free not only to write on the worksheets and charts, but also to underline and highlight things, and to write comments and questions in the margins. By the time you have finished with a workbook, it should look well and truly used.

- You will also find lots of space in the main text. These are for you to write down your thoughts and ideas, and your responses to the questions.

- Keep an open mind and be willing to experiment with new ideas and skills. These books will sometimes ask you to think about painful issues. However, if anxiety is distressing you and restricting your life, it really is worth making the effort to overcome it. The rewards will be substantial.

- Be prepared to invest time in doing the practical exercises – set aside 20 to 30 minutes each day if you can. You can maintain your achievements by practising your coping skills regularly and knowing how to learn from setbacks.

- Try to answer all the questions and do the exercises, even if you have to come back to some of them later. There may be times when you get stuck and can't think how to take things forward. If this happens, don't get angry with yourself or give up. Just put the book aside and come back to it later, when you are feeling more relaxed.

- You may find it helpful to work through the books with a friend. Two heads are often better than one. And you may be able to encourage each other to persist, even when one of you is finding it hard. Ask for the help of family and friends, particularly in the practical tasks.

- Re-read the workbook. You may get more out of it once you've had a chance to think about some of the ideas and put them into practice for a little while.

- Each workbook builds on what has already been covered. So what you learn when working with one will help you when you come to the next. It's quite possible simply to dip into different ones as you please, but you may get most out of the series if you follow them through systematically, step by step.

What if I don't feel better?

There is nothing to lose by working through this book; it will give you practical coping skills you can put into practice straight away. However, if you find that self-help alone is not meeting your needs (this is sometimes the case), see your family doctor, medical practitioner or specialist therapist, who can offer extra support. If you do need to seek more help this doesn't mean you have failed in any way; just that your difficulties are perhaps more complex.

A note of caution

These workbooks will not help everyone who has problem worries, fears and anxieties. If you find that focusing on anxiety is actually making you feel worse instead of better, you may be suffering from clinical depression. The recognized signs of clinical depression include:

- Constantly feeling sad, down, depressed or empty

- General lack of interest in what's going on around you

- A big increase or decrease in your appetite and weight

- A marked change in your sleep patterns

- Noticeable speeding up or slowing down in your movements and how you go about things

- Feeling of being tired and low in energy

- An intense sense of guilt or worthlessness

- Difficulty in concentrating and making decisions

- A desire to hurt yourself or a feeling that you might be better off dead

If you have had five or more of these symptoms (including low mood or loss of interest) for two weeks or more, you should seek professional help from a doctor, counsellor or psychotherapist. There is nothing shameful about seeking this sort of professional help – any more than there is anything shameful about taking your car to a garage if it is not working as it should, or going to see a lawyer if you have legal problems. It simply means taking your journey towards self-knowledge and self-acceptance with the help of a friendly guide, rather than striking out alone.

SECTION 1: Managing Avoidance – Graded Practice

As Part One explained, avoidance and escape are common responses to anxiety. People fear many different things – heights, arguments, public speaking – but whatever makes you anxious, avoiding it will maintain your fear. In this section you will learn how to use graded practice to face your fear instead of avoiding or running away from it.

Although you will, ultimately, have to face your fear, it can be best to pace yourself and not take on *too* much too soon. Graded practice is a step by step technique for overcoming the urge to avoid or run away from the things that make you anxious. It is especially useful if you suffer from a phobia of some kind. In *graded* practice you build up to facing your greatest anxiety through gradual steps, so that you never need to feel too scared. You build on successful experiences, systematically challenging your old belief that something is threatening.

The later sections will help you with other skills.

Remember to continue to practise your breathing skills, relaxation skills and thought challenging skills described in Part Two to help build your ability to cope with difficult situations.

Facing fear through graded practice

There are four stages in graded practice:

1 Identifying the trigger for your anxiety

2 Setting targets

3 Grading tasks

4 Practising challenging your fear

Describe your fear

Step one is to describe your anxiety trigger in specific detail. You might have a phobia of spiders, for instance, but this could mean very different things to different people. You might be able to cope with a medium-sized spider at the other side of the room, and only become frightened if that spider moved nearer. Another person would become panicky just looking at a picture of a spider.

Dissect your anxiety triggers

A good way to start thinking about the things that trigger your anxiety in detail is to ask questions. Look at the three examples below.

CASE STUDY 1: Sylvia has a spider phobia

Sylvia needs to ask herself questions such as:

* What size of spider makes me feel anxious?

* How near can I tolerate the spider?

* Does it make a difference where I am, or what time of day it happens to be?

* Does it make a difference if I am with someone?

When you have answered these sorts of questions for yourself, you will be able to describe your fear in more detail. You might discover that your anxiety is only triggered by large spiders, and that you can tolerate medium-sized or small ones. You might not be able to bear a large spider in the same room as yourself, but you are fairly comfortable if you know one is in another room. You might learn that you are more afraid of spiders at night, when you can't see them. And you might feel much less anxious when you have someone with you.

You would then be able to describe your anxiety more exactly as 'a fear of being in the same room as a large spider, especially when alone at night.'

CASE STUDY 2: Annette has a fear of shopping

Annette needs to ask herself questions such as:

* Which shops make me particularly anxious?

* What time of the day is worse or better for me?

* What makes it easier or harder for me to cope?

If you do this for yourself, you might then re-describe your problem as being 'a fear of large supermarkets (but not small shops) which is worse during the busy times of the day'. You might also add that you find it easier to shop if you have a friend with you, and if you have planned your shopping trip thoroughly beforehand.

CASE STUDY 3: Peter has a fear of public speaking

Peter needs to ask himself questions such as:

- What settings make me particularly anxious?
- What sort of audience or subject matter disturbs me most?
- What makes it easier or harder for me to cope?

When you ask yourself these questions you might discover that your problem is 'a fear of speaking in front of an audience of a dozen or so in a semi-formal setting'. You might find that you are not fearful of small, informal discussions or of large, very formal lectures when you read from a script. You might also realize that it is more difficult for you if you are already stressed – when you are abroad, for example, or very tired. You might find it easier if you have a colleague sharing the responsibility and if you have planned your presentation thoroughly beforehand.

Now think about your own fear(s) and what the triggers might be (you may need to return to the diaries you kept as part of your exercises in Part Two). Ask yourself the questions in the templates below and record precise descriptions. You may have more than one fear, so do this exercise for each of them.

Fear 1

My fear or anxiety is:

_____

_____

_____

What place or setting makes my fear worse?

_____

_____

_____

At what time of day or night is my fear worse?

_____

_____

_____

Do people make my fear better or worse?

_____

_____

_____

What makes it easier or harder for me to cope?

_____

_____

_____

Fear 2

My fear or anxiety is:

_____

_____

_____

What place or setting makes my fear worse?

_____

_____

_____

At what time of day or night is my fear worse?

_____

_____

_____

Do people make my fear better or worse?

_____

_____

_____

What makes it easier or harder for me to cope?

_____

_____

_____

Fear 3

My fear or anxiety is:

_____

_____

_____

What place or setting makes my fear worse?

_____

_____

_____

_____

At what time of day or night is my fear worse?

_____

_____

_____

Do people make my fear better or worse?

_____

_____

_____

What makes it easier or harder for me to cope?

_____

_____

_____

_____

The answers to these questions will help you come up with a systematic plan to challenge your fear. This means facing the fear one step at a time by changing one aspect of your feared situation at a time.

It may seem frightening to face your fear, but you will do this gradually so that you never need feel very afraid. Graded practice helps you learn that certain situations or things are not really dangerous – in this way you can challenge your beliefs and fears and build up your confidence.

Setting targets

Look at your descriptions of your fears. If you have several arrange them in the order of greatest fear to lowest fear. These specific descriptions of your fear or anxiety will now become the target you want to work towards facing. The list below is an example of how these targets might look for Annette who feels very anxious in crowds.

Making a list of targets

Greatest fear

1 Shopping in the hypermarket, alone, on Friday evening, when it is most busy.

2 Taking the bus from home into town (four miles), alone, in the morning when the bus is crowded.

3 Using the elevator at work (from the bottom floor to level seven) when there is nobody around.

Lowest fear

4 Sitting in the centre of the row at a movie or in a theatre, with my partner.

Find your motivation

Only list targets which you want to achieve, as these will be the ones which you are most motivated to tackle. You don't have to take on every target which presents a challenge, only those which are relevant to you. For example, you might well be frightened by the idea of walking a tightrope, but if it does not make a difference to your life and you really don't want to walk a tightrope, you don't have to make it a target just because it is frightening.

Write your list in the space below:

Greatest fear

1 _____

_____

_____

_____

2 _____

_____

_____

_____

3 _____

_____

_____

_____

Lowest fear

4 _____

_____

_____

_____

Choosing a target to tackle

When you have your targets ranked according to difficulty, select the easiest one to start with. However, if one of the targets is particularly urgent, you might have to begin with that one instead. At this stage, you should only tackle one target at a time. You will then need to work out a way of achieving this target in small, safe, graded steps or *tasks*.

Grading tasks

The key step in graded practice is to break down your target into a series of manageable tasks that very gradually become more difficult. The first task has to be manageable, so ask yourself:

‘Can I imagine myself doing this with effort?’

If you answer ‘no’ then make the task easier.

It is very important that you do not take excessive risks: the aim of graded practice is to build on a series of successes, so you have to plan for success. In describing your fear, you asked yourself the question: ‘What makes it easier for me?’ Now you can include as many of these factors as possible in order to increase the likelihood that the earlier tasks will be manageable. Later, you can increase the difficulty of the tasks so that you ensure that you build up your self-confidence. For example, in the early stages of tackling a fear, you might find it easier to face it with a friend, at a quiet time. If you were to continue to use your friend and to avoid busy times, you would not overcome your fear, but it is an ideal starting point for going on to develop greater independence.

Each task should be described in detail. Look at the example below.

Annette: A fear of shopping

Annette's target
Shopping in the hypermarket, alone, on Friday evening.

Tasks

1 Shopping in the local store, with my friend Bill, on Thursday afternoon, when it is quiet. Buying just one item, which I can pick up easily and take to the shop-keeper. I will have the correct money in my hand.

2 I'll repeat step one but I'll buy three items which I can pick up easily and pay by credit card so that I have to wait for the transaction.

3 This time I will buy at least ten items from a shopping list and pay by credit card.

This is the starting point for graded practice; the tasks could develop in various ways before reaching the target.

For example, Annette could start to shop on her own and build on that, or could begin to take on larger stores, or could start shopping at busier times.

Only one aspect of the task should be changed at a time and the choice of task would depend on what was most manageable and on practical constraints. For example, if Bill were only available for a short time, Annette would try to become independent of him before changing the task to a busier time or a larger store.

Each task presents an opportunity to use your coping skills (relaxation, controlled breathing, distraction, challenging).

Here is the rest of Annette's graded practice.

Tasks

4 Using the local shop, at a quiet time on my own.

5 Using the local store, alone, at a medium-busy time.

6 Using the local store, alone, at the busiest time.

7   Using a mini-market, alone, at a quiet time.

8   Using a mini-market, alone, at a busy time.

9   Using the supermarket, alone, at a quiet time.

10   Using the supermarket, alone, at a busy time.

11   Using the hypermarket, alone, at a quiet time.

12   Using the hypermarket, alone, at a busy time.

Now try breaking down your target into small, specific tasks.

Target:

_____

_____

_____

_____

Tasks

1   _____

_____

_____

2   _____

_____

_____

3   _____

_____

_____

4 _____
 _____
 _____

5 _____
 _____
 _____

6 _____
 _____
 _____

7 _____
 _____
 _____

Practising

Rehearse each step, using your coping skills (for example, challenging worrying thoughts), until you can manage it without difficulty; then move on to the next task, and so on. Don't be put off by some feelings of anxiety – these are only natural, because you are learning to master anxiety instead of avoiding it. To be helpful, practice has to be:

- regular and frequent enough for the benefits not to be lost

- rewarding – recognize your achievements and learn to praise yourself

- repeated until the anxiety is no longer there

- reflected upon – ask yourself 'what have I learnt from this?' As you repeatedly discover that you can cope, you will build your confidence.

Each subsequent task should change by only a small amount, for example you could change the number of people present, or the time of day, or your distance from the trigger, but not all three at once.

By working through these small, specific steps, you can eventually reach your target.

To give you an example, here is what a list of graded tasks would look like for Sylvia who has a fear of spiders:

CASE STUDY: Sylvia

'I've always been scared of spiders and I became really worried that I'd pass this on to my children. So, I asked a friend to help me overcome my fears by making me face spiders. She wasn't spider-phobic and so she was able to catch a really big one and keep it in a jar for me to get used to. I soon realized that, as long as there was a choice, I would not go near that spider. That's why she surprised me one day by putting the thing right in front of me. I say surprised me, but it really terrified me and I burst into tears and my fear was greater than ever.

'Next, I asked my doctor what I should do and she explained that I'd done the right thing in trying to face my fear, but that I could have gone about this in a much more gradual fashion. With her help, I described my fear very precisely and then we drew up a series of steps with the final goal of me being able to tolerate a spider in the corner of the room. She also taught me a relaxation exercise which I was to use to calm myself while I was carrying out the practice.

My fear: *Being alone in a room with a large spider (with a diameter of more than 2 cm), particularly if I am in the bedroom in the dark.*

Target: *To sit in my living room, on my own, with a 2 cm spider somewhere loose in the room.*

Step 1:   With my friend, sitting in the living room with a 1 cm dead spider, in the corner. Tolerate this until my anxiety is low.

Step 2:   With my friend, sitting in the living room with a 2 cm dead spider, in the corner. Tolerate this until my anxiety is low.

Step 3:   With my friend, sitting in the living room with a 2 cm dead spider 2 m away. Tolerate this until my anxiety is low.

Step 4:   With my friend, sitting in the living room with a 2 cm dead spider 1 m away. Tolerate this until my anxiety is low.

Step 5:   With my friend, sitting in the living room with a 2 cm dead spider next to me. Tolerate this until my anxiety is low.

Step 6:   With my friend, sitting in the living room with a 1 cm live spider in a jar in the corner. Tolerate this until my anxiety is low.

Step 7:   With my friend, sitting in the living room with a 2 cm live spider in a jar in the corner. Tolerate this until my anxiety is low.

Step 8:   With my friend, sitting in the living room with a 2 cm live spider in a jar 2 m away. Tolerate this until my anxiety is low.

Step 9:   With my friend, sitting in the living room with a 2 cm live spider in a jar 1 m away. Tolerate this until my anxiety is low.

Step 10:   With my friend, sitting in the living room with a 2 cm live spider in a jar next to me. Tolerate this until my anxiety is low.

Step 11:   With my friend, sitting in the living room with a 2 cm live spider somewhere in the room. Tolerate this until my anxiety is low.

Step 12:   Alone in the living room with a 2 cm live spider, somewhere in the room. Tolerate this until my anxiety is low.

'I felt reassured by this gentler plan and, luckily, my friend was still willing to help me so we both practised the relaxation exercises and then began at step 1. The doctor had checked with me that this step was something that I felt that I could achieve and so it was no surprise that it seemed easy. We moved on to steps 2 and 3 in the same day. Each time I progressed, I asked myself "What have I just learned?" and each time I could tell myself that I had learnt that I could tolerate being near a spider and that I could cope better than I had predicted. Step 4 was rather more taxing and I had to practise this a few times before I could relax myself; and I did wonder if step 5 wasn't over-ambitious as we had to go over this many times: with hindsight, I should have put in an extra step some-where between 4 and 5. In contrast, steps 6 and 7 seemed hardly necessary once I had learnt to tolerate the dead spider so close. As I reflected on my progress I began to revise my self-concept. I found myself reassuring myself with the thought: "I can cope, I have coped in the past and discovered that nothing terrible happens". Within a few weeks, I had reached my goal and the children are really pleased with me, which is the biggest reward.'

Difficulties in using graded practice

'I can't keep going: I keep failing'

If you find that a task is too difficult, don't give up or feel that you have failed. Instead, look for ways of making the task easier – perhaps as two or three smaller steps. Expect setbacks from time to time – this is only natural – and, when it happens, think about your task. Did you overestimate what you could do and make the task too difficult? Did you practise when you were feeling unwell or tired? Did you have other things on your mind so that you could not put enough effort into your practice? If you keep a record of your practice, you can more easily work out why you have difficulties on certain days. Each setback will tell you more about your particular needs: it is an opportunity to learn more about your particular fear.

'I'm not getting anywhere'

As you move up your hierarchy of tasks, it is all too easy to downgrade or fail to appreciate your progress. By keeping a diary like the one on the facing page (there are blank diary sheets at the back of this Part) you will create a record of your achievements and you can review this as a reminder of your progress. Rate the degree of anxiety you feel when you perform each task. In column 4, 'Other relevant information', you might like to note what made the task easier of more difficult, or if you had to repeat the task several times.

Don't forget to give yourself credit for your achievements, no matter how small. Try not to downgrade your successes and try not to criticize yourself: encouragement works better. In this way, you will manage to reach your goals and face your fears with confidence.

Diary

Date	Task	Anxiety rating (1–10)	Other relevant information

Summary

1 Everyone has different fears: get to know just what your fears are and describe them very specifically. These are your targets.

2 Rank the targets in order of ease or priority. Take the first one.

3 Reduce the target to a series of achievable steps. Take no excessive risks – you are planning to build on success.

4 Practise each step regularly, reflect on your progress and reward yourself each time you master your task.

SECTION 2: Problem-Solving

Graded practice is the way of facing your fear if you have time to organize a programme for yourself. If you only have a short time, because a situation has arisen at short notice, or because you didn't get yourself organized in time, a problem-solving approach can help.

The problem-solving approach can help you to focus your thinking so that you devise solutions to your dilemma rather than panic in the face of it. There are six steps in problem-solving:

1 Defining the problem

2 Listing solutions

3 Evaluating the pros and cons of the solutions

4 Choosing a solution and planning to put it into action

5 Doing it

6 Reviewing the outcome

1 Define the problem

Be specific about the challenge that faces you, and try not to confuse two or more different problems. Where possible, distinguish the different aspects of your problem and separate it into a collection of more manageable tasks. Then make a plan for each. For example, this is Sally's worry about an approaching wedding:

> 'I have to attend Mary's wedding next week and stand beside her as her best friend. Afterwards, I'll have to go to a reception.'

This might reflect several problems:

1 'I have to deal with my claustrophobia in the church. This means being able to stand behind Mary for at least twenty minutes, in a confined space and without the support of my partner.'

2 'I have to cope with being a focus of attention for several hours, without having a panic attack.'

3 'I am expected to attend a reception of about fifty guests. This will last for three or four hours and will be in the marquee. I will have to cope with my anxiety.'

Once you have defined your task(s), select one and ask yourself:

● What is going to happen?

● When will this happen?

● Who is involved?

Work only on one task – don't try to problem-solve more than one difficulty at a time. Select your task and state your goal in very specific terms. Example 1, below, describes Sally's wedding problem, while example 2 focuses on a different type of difficulty, which Sally needs to face quickly.

Example 1: 'I have to deal with my claustrophobia in the church. This means being able to stand behind Mary for at least twenty minutes, in a confined space and without the support of my partner.'

Example 2: 'I have to see my boss about a rise in pay within two days or lose the chance of an increase in salary.'

Defining your problem

In the space below write down the particular problem you have to face. Answer the questions to help you define it precisely.

My problem:

_____

_____

_____

_____

What is going to happen?

_____

_____

When will this happen?

Who is involved?

2 List solutions

Think of as many ways of dealing with the problem as you can, _without censoring your ideas_. At this stage, you are aiming to produce a wide range of possible courses of action. You will slow down the process if you try to judge your responses. The more solutions you come up with the better. Write down all your ideas, no matter how trivial or outrageous they might seem, as some of your 'trivial' or 'outrageous' solutions might turn out to be most useful. In order to increase the range of your responses, it might be helpful to put yourself in someone else's shoes and consider how that person would respond if asked to deal with your problem. Look at Sally's list of possible solutions as an example.

CASE STUDY: Problem-solving in action 1

Problem

'I have to deal with my claustrophobia in the church. This means being able to stand behind Mary for at least twenty minutes, in a confined space and without the support of my partner.'

Solutions

Send my apologies, with an explanation of my problem

Send my daughter in my place

Recall how I coped at the last wedding and try to use these coping strategies again

Plan 'escape routes' which I could use if I found my anxiety was too great during the reception

Talk all my fears through with my friend – it puts things in perspective

Ignore the invitation

CASE STUDY: Problem-solving in action 2

Problem

'I have to see my boss about a rise in pay within two days or lose the chance of an increase in salary.'

Solutions

Quit to avoid the confrontation

Ask a colleague how I might phrase my request

Ask my friend to rehearse with me what I might say

Have several lunchtime drinks to give me courage

Prepare myself by relaxing before I see my boss

Ask for a time extension so that I am better able to prepare

Decide to keep quiet and miss the opportunity of a rise this year

Your own list of solutions

In the space below write your own list of solutions.

Problem:

_____

_____

Solutions:

_____

_____

_____

_____

_____

_____

_____

_____

_____

_____

_____

3 Look at the pros and cons of each solution

At this point, you need to consider each of your solutions and decide which will have to be rejected because they are unsuitable or impossible. Then look at the remainder and rank in order the solutions according to usefulness for you at this time. Look at Sally's list as an example.

CASE STUDY: Problem-solving in action 1

Problem

'I have to deal with my claustrophobia in the church. This means being able to stand behind Mary for at least twenty minutes, in a confined space and without the support of my partner.'

Reject

Ignore the invitation
Send my daughter in my place

Accept

1st: Recall how I coped at the last wedding and try to use these coping strategies again
2nd: Talk all my fears through with my friend – it puts things in perspective
3rd: Plan 'escape routes' which I could use if I found my anxiety was too great during the reception
4th: Send my apologies, with an explanation of my problem

CASE STUDY: Problem-solving in action 2

Problem

'I have to see my boss about a rise in pay within two days or lose the chance of an increase in salary.'

Reject

Quit to avoid the confrontation
Have several lunchtime drinks to give me courage

Accept

1st: Ask a colleague how I might phrase my request
2nd: Ask my friend to rehearse with me what I might say
3rd: Prepare myself by relaxing before I see my boss
4th: Ask for a time extension so that I am better able to prepare
5th: Decide to keep quiet and miss the opportunity of a rise this year

In the space below write down which solutions you must reject and which you can accept.

Your revised list of solutions

Reject:

_____

_____

_____

_____

Accept:

_____

_____

_____

_____

_____

_____

_____

_____

4 Choose a solution and plan to put it into action

When you have done this, simply take your first-choice solution and start to plan how to put it into action.

In very specific and concrete terms, decide how you are going to implement your chosen solution. Be sure to answer the following questions:

- What will be done?

- How will it be done?

- When will it be done?

- Who is involved?

- Where will it take place?

- What is my contingency plan?

A contingency plan is a back-up plan which you can put into operation if your task is more difficult than you anticipated or something unexpected turns up and prevents you from carrying through your original course of action. For example, you might carry the telephone number of a friend whom you can ring to collect you from the wedding, or to whom you could talk if you got nervous just before your interview with your boss. Look at the examples below for ideas.

CASE STUDY: Problem-solving in action 1

Task: Recall how I coped at the last wedding and try to use these coping strategies again

'I will sit in my study, where I shan't be disturbed, and I will try to recall all the details of the last wedding I attended. I will then write down all the strategies that I can remember using to help me get through that reception. If I find that I cannot remember enough or if I am disturbed too often to be able to do this task, I will try solution 2.'

CASE STUDY: Problem-solving in action 2

Task: Ask a colleague how I might phrase my request

'I will telephone Robert this evening and explain my situation, and I will ask him what he would say to his boss if he were to argue for a pay rise. I will wait until the kids are in bed because I don't want to be disturbed by them. If Robert is not helpful or is not at home, my back-up will be Rose – I'll try her next. If she is not able to help, I can try Jean.'

Where possible, rehearse dealing with your task, either in imagination or with someone who could role-play with you. Also, scan all your solutions to see if you might profitably combine them. For example, you might find that 'Asking my friend to rehearse with me what I might say' combines well with 'Preparing myself by relaxing before I see my boss'.

Your own action plan

In the space below write your own action plan by answering the questions.

What will I do?

_____

_____

_____

How will I do it?

_____

When will I do it?

Who is involved?

Where will it take place?

What could go wrong?

What is my contingency plan?

5 Do it

Try out your solution, making sure that contingency plans are in place and that you are properly prepared both physically and mentally. Whether or not you regard your action as successful, review it and see what you can learn.

6 Review the outcome

If your solution works and is sufficient, congratulate yourself and remember this successful experience for the future. Ask yourself why it was successful: what did you learn about your strengths and needs? Use successful experiences to challenge your anxious beliefs. Write your response below.

My solution was successful because:

_____

_____

_____

_____

My strengths and needs are:

_____

_____

_____

_____

If your solution does not solve your problem, try to understand why it didn't – perhaps you were over-ambitious, perhaps you were not feeling strong that day, perhaps you misjudged someone else's response to you. Whatever conclusion you reach, remember that you did *not fail*. Expect some disappointments, but commend yourself for having tried. Learn as much as you can from the experience and reflect on what you would do differently with hindsight. Then go back to your solution list and select the next one.

My solution did not work because:

_____

_____

_____

_____

What I would do differently next time:

_____

_____

_____

_____

You can continue to return to your list of solutions as often as you need to. The more solutions you are able to come up with, the greater will be your store of options.

Problem-solving is a useful technique when you find yourself in a situation which requires prompt action. However, it is always better to plan well in advance if you can; so try not to put off thinking about a difficult task until the last moment.

Difficulties in using problem-solving

'My solution didn't work and I didn't know what to do!'

Remember how important it is to prepare thoroughly. Thorough brainstorming is essential to problem-solving; without this, you will be short of solutions and contingency plans. When you do make specific plans for action, always ask yourself what could go wrong and prepare a back-up solution. If you do this, you should be able to devise a coping plan even if your chosen solution doesn't work.

'I can't possibly include such unhelpful solutions as avoidance and using alcohol'

Why not? If the time isn't right for you to tackle the problem head-on, it is time for you to use a compromise solution. Provided you have tried other ways of coping before resorting to your 'unhelpful' solution, accept that you have tried your best. Sometimes we all have to handle difficulties in ways which aren't entirely satisfactory to us. With time and practice in dealing with problem situations, you will be better able to use strategies with which you are happier.

Summary

1 When a problem is immediate, you can tackle it by using a structured 'problem-solving' approach.

2 This involves six steps: defining the problem; listing solutions; evaluating the pros and cons of the solutions; choosing a solution and planning to implement it; implementing your chosen solution; evaluating your performance.

3 If your chosen solution does not work, choose another from your list and repeat the six steps. Be prepared to compromise.

SECTION 3: **Being Assertive**

Assertiveness is another skill which can help you manage worry, fear and anxiety. Being assertive is a way of communicating your needs, feelings or rights to others while being respectful and without infringing their rights.

Some people find it difficult to be assertive because they do not recognize their basic entitlements. These include the right to:

- ask for what you want
- say 'No'
- have opinions, feelings and emotions
- make your own decisions
- ask for clarification
- make mistakes
- change your mind
- be private
- be independent.

Read through the list again and put a cross next to any point you feel you don't feel you have the right to. If you put a cross against several points you may benefit from working at becoming more assertive.

In learning to be assertive you will develop the ability to communicate these rights in a way which is clear and respectful of yourself and of others. This means not being passive, nor aggressive, nor manipulative, as these positions are not mutually respectful.

- The *passive* type of person opts out of conflict, can't make decisions and aims always to please others. This can be a very frustrating position because the passive person never respects personal needs. At best, this could leave a person disappointed, and at worst feeling resentful and thwarted.

- The *aggressive* type appears loud and forceful, belittling the thoughts, actions and personal qualities of others. An aggressive person must win, has no time for the feelings or rights of others and has no reservation about behaving selfishly and attacking unfairly. At best, this type of person gets what he or she wants but can hurt others and damage relationships in the process.

- The *manipulative* type is indirectly aggressive and controlling. In this case, the attack is concealed. Thus, this person may *appear* to be supportive and understanding, but will use emotional blackmail and will subtly undermine the other person in order to achieve a selfish goal.

- The *assertive* type, by contrast to all the other types, sees both sides of a situation and recognizes the rights and needs of all parties. An assertive person takes responsibility for his or her own actions and does not need to put down others or her/himself in order to feel comfortable.

The goal of assertive behaviour is to confront without undermining oneself or others, whereas the goal of passive behaviour is to avoid conflict and the goal of aggressive or manipulative behaviour is to win. Passivity and aggression are easy to spot, while the manipulative person is less easy to recognize as an aggressor.

Read through the following examples and circle the term that correctly applies in each case.

1 'Turn that down or I'll put my foot through your hi-fi.'

Assertive   *Aggressive*   *Manipulative*   *Passive*

2 'This programme is boring me – you can watch it if you want but I'm going to bed.'

Assertive   *Aggressive*   *Manipulative*   *Passive*

3 'Let's just watch whatever you want to watch.'

Assertive   *Aggressive*   *Manipulative*   *Passive*

4 'Maybe if you stopped nagging I'd get round to it.'

Assertive   *Aggressive*   *Manipulative*   *Passive*

5 'Your car is blocking my drive – I'd like you to move it.'

Assertive   *Aggressive*   *Manipulative*   *Passive*

6 'Give me a raise or I quit.'

Assertive   Aggressive   Manipulative   Passive

7 'It bothers me but I don't want to get involved.'

Assertive   Aggressive   Manipulative   Passive

8 'You said that you would be finished by Wednesday so please make sure it's ready by then.'

Assertive   Aggressive   Manipulative   Passive

Numbers 1 and 6 are aggressive.

Numbers 2 and 4 are manipulative – the speaker is trying to get what he or she wants by complaining or insulting the other person, without respecting their feelings or being honest/straightforward about what he or she wants.

Numbers 3 and 7 are passive.

Numbers 5 and 8 are assertive – the speaker is being firm but polite, stating facts not opinions and being straightforward about what he or she wants.

Asserting yourself

Being assertive involves five steps:

1 Decide what you *want*: in other words, respect your own needs, desires and rights.

2 Decide if what you want is *fair*: in other words, respect other people's rights.

3 Ask for it *clearly*. This means preparing your statement well.

4 Be prepared to take *risks*. You might have to tolerate discomfort and uncertainty.

5 Keep *calm*. This is where your other anxiety management skills come in – draw on the strategies you have learned to maintain physical and mental calmness.

Prepare to be assertive

Brief yourself so that you know that your arguments are sound. Your argument does not have to be long and complicated to be sound: simple explanations and requests can be effective. Script your argument in advance and organize it in terms of the *explanation*, your *feelings*, your *needs* and the *consequences* (both *positive and negative*). Read Maxine's script below for an example.

CASE STUDY: Maxine

Maxine lives on an estate where there are lots of families with young children. Recently they have started playing football outside her apartment and Maxine is stressed because they are damaging her garden and she has started to feel like a prisoner in her own home. She realizes that she needs to speak with them. Determined to be assertive, she draws up a script of the arguments she could use:

The explanation: *'I want to discuss a problem with you. In the last few weeks, you have been playing ball near to my fence and the ball often comes into my garden. In reclaiming the ball, you often damage my flowers.'*

Your feelings: *'Although I realize that you are not doing this on purpose and that you are just playing, I am tired of arriving home to find the garden trampled.'*

Your needs: *'Therefore, I would appreciate it if you played elsewhere.'*

The consequences: *'If you do, I'd be very grateful (positive), otherwise I will have to talk to your parents about it (negative).'*

Top tips for being assertive

- *Be positive:* a safe way of beginning is by using a compliment or a positive statement, for example 'This is an excellent piece of work, but I would like you to write more clearly so that it is easier for me to read next time.' 'That is a very good idea, but I don't think that it would work here.'

- *Be objective:* do not get involved in personal criticism, but do explain the situation as you see it. Never criticize the person, only the behaviour.

- *Be brief:* in order to avoid the other person switching off, butting in or side-tracking, be succinct. Just describe the facts.

- *Be aware of manipulative criticism:* don't expect that others will always be cooperative and accept your point. Although you might get an agreement, this is not always the case. The other person could try to distract you and undermine your efforts by using manipulative criticism. This may either take the form of appearing to be caring, whilst undermining you, or it could be direct criticism.

Writing your own script

Think of a situation (recent if possible) where you wanted to be assertive but were
unable to be. Now, try drafting a script for yourself, writing down the four stages of
your argument:

The problem:

_____

_____

Your explanation:

_____

_____

_____

Your feelings:

_____

_____

Your needs:

_____

_____

The consequences:

_____

_____

You can prepare scripts in advance of any situation where you know that you want
to be assertive. Try out your scripts on a friend if this helps to boost your confidence
(there are extra blank scripts at the end of this Part). The more confident you are,
the more effective you will be in confronting the sources of your anxiety.

Dealing with manipulative criticism

Imagine that you had asserted that your boss gave you too much work to do. You had thought this through and discussed it with a friend, and, although you recognized that the department was very busy, you still felt that you were being unreasonably burdened. Your boss, rather than respecting your statement, reacts by using manipulative criticism such as:

- *Nagging*
  'Never mind that, haven't you finished yet? Your problem is that you are too slow. Now get on with the job.'

- *Caring*
  'That's all very well, but I really do think that it is in your best interest to improve your skills by carrying a substantial workload.'

- *Lecturing*
  'Well, quite *obviously* the real problem is … and you should…'

- *Insults*
  'Typical woman: can't cope in the real world.'

- *Concern*
  'If you are having these problems, are you sure you're right for this job, after all?'

- *Advice*
  'Let me tell you what I would do if I were you…'

- *Expert advice*
  'Believe me, I know what sort of a person you are and what's best for you, so you should…'

- *Hurt*
  'You've made me feel terrible…'

Each of these responses is aimed at undermining your needs and your rights, they are intended to deflect your argument. To deal with this, you will need to develop skills in standing your ground. There are two particularly useful approaches which will help you to be more assertive and handle manipulative criticism: the 'broken record' and fielding criticism.

1 *The broken record*

An unassertive person takes 'No' for an answer far too easily and is not persistent in making a point. A basic assertiveness skill is being persistent and repeating what you want over and over again – calmly: like a broken record.

Once you have decided that what you want to say is fair, go ahead and assert it. Repeat your message until the other person accepts it or agrees to negotiate with you.

This is a particularly useful approach when dealing with situations where:

- your rights are clearly in danger of being abused

- where you are likely to be put off by irrelevant arguments

- where you feel vulnerable because you know the other person will use criticism to undermine your self-esteem.

Once you have prepared your 'script' you can relax and repeat your argument. You know exactly what you are going to say, however abusive or manipulative the other person tries to be.

2 *Fielding criticism*

This is particularly helpful in dealing with manipulative criticism that might otherwise leave you feeling so badly about yourself that you agree to do something that you would rather not.

There is often an element of truth in what is being said, but it is exaggerated. For example: 'Typical! You're always late... insensitive... selfish... expect others to do your work...' might well make you feel guilty, even though the only truth in the statement is 'you are late'.

You can field criticism by calmly acknowledging that there may be some truth in what has been said. It can be left at that, if you do not want to get into a dialogue; or you may follow up with an assertion of your view, if you still have a point to make. Fielding also keeps the situation calm and allows you some time to think clearly.

On the next page are some examples of fielding the comments made by the difficult boss earlier.

Criticism	Response
'Typical woman: can't cope in the real world!'	'That's right. I can't cope and that is why I am asking you to recognize that you give me too much to do.'
'Never mind that, haven't you finished yet? Your problem is that you are too slow. Now get on with the job.'	'You are right, I am too slow, given the amount of work that I have to deal with, and that is why I am asking you to recognize that you give me too much to do.'
'You've made me feel terrible.'	'I am sorry that you feel terrible but I still want you to recognize that you give me too much to do.'

Negotiating

The aim of being assertive is not to win at all costs, but to reach a solution that is reasonable to all parties. This will involve compromise and negotiation. Negotiating is easier if you:

- Ask for the argument to be clearly *defined*. It is important that you understand the issue and are aware of the other person's position, reasoning and needs.

- *Keep calm* by using controlled breathing and adopting a relaxed attitude.

- *Prepare*. If you have time, do your homework – get the facts to support your case and rehearse your script. Consider how far you are prepared to compromise.

- *Acknowledge the other side of the argument* (for example 'I understand your position, but…'); try to empathize with the other person (i.e. put yourself in his or her shoes).

- *Never attack* the person, only the behaviour with which you disagree.

- *Keep to the point*. Don't get led away from your argument: make your point and repeat yourself as often as is necessary.

- *Take risks* and be prepared to *compromise*. Do not be stubborn and determined to win at all costs: this is what aggressive people do.

As a beginner

Being assertive isn't too difficult once you are aware of, and have practised, these strategies. When you're inexperienced, however, it is crucial to plan and rehearse, otherwise it easy to unintentionally become aggressive, manipulative or passive.

Remember that assertiveness is a skill and it improves with training and practice. You might find that it pays to go to a class. See if there are assertiveness training classes in your area.

As with each of the other skills that we have covered, reflect on your progress and consider what you are learning about your ability to engage in difficult situations. Use this to challenge your anxious beliefs.

Read Karen's story below on how she used assertiveness to manage her social phobia.

CASE STUDY: Karen

'A bus driver humiliated me because I didn't have the right money for my ticket. Right in front of twenty passengers, he called me names and finally yelled: "Get the right money or get off the bus. Now!" I just stood by the side of the road crying as the bus drove away.

'The next day, I avoided using the bus and I walked into town. I was still upset and anxious so when an assistant in the delicatessen was brusque with me, I simply fled without finishing my shopping. After that I stopped going out alone.

'Fortunately, I found a local assertiveness training class which helped me to learn that I could regain my confidence. I worked my way up to taking a bus into town. On the day that I tackled that task, I really did not have the correct money for the fare. I thought about it and decided that it was reasonable for me to ask for a ticket anyway. I prepared my speech: "I realize that you ask passengers to have the correct money for the fare, but I have been unable to find it today. I appreciate that you might not be able to give me change, but if you could, I would be very grateful." I had also prepared myself in case the driver was hostile; I had planned to say: "I made a reasonable request and I am sorry that you haven't respected that. I am perfectly prepared to walk but shall report your conduct to the director of the bus company." I practised these phrases until I felt confident with them.

'In the end it all went smoothly and the driver let me travel without a fuss! I learned that I have got the ability to stand up to people and confront difficult situations.'

Difficulties in being assertive

'I get too nervous at the last minute'

It is not unusual to feel anxious when you are about to tackle a difficult situation, but you can take steps to minimize your fear.

- It always helps to start with the least threatening situation and work up to the more difficult challenges, developing your confidence as you go.

- Prepare yourself by rehearsing.

- Have a contingency plan for coping if things do not go smoothly (see page 23).

- Use the strategies that you learnt in Part Two to help you keep calm.

'I had to back down and didn't get what I wanted'

The aim of being assertive is not to win (although this may be a bonus) but to reach a reasonable conclusion. Good planning and practice will increase your chances of success, but you should always be ready to compromise, and accept that sometimes you will encounter someone who is too aggressive to be respectful of your position. Give yourself credit for taking on the challenge in the first place.

Summary

1 Familiarize yourself with your basic rights.

2 Decide what you want or need and review this in the context of your rights and the rights of others.

3 Rehearse your arguments.

4 Be prepared to have to repeat yourself, handle criticism and negotiate.

5 Always review your progress and what you have learnt about yourself and your fears.

SECTION 4: Time Management

Many people identify time pressures as a major source of stress – not having enough time to do everything; needing to do things too quickly; always being in a rush; never having a chance to relax. Time pressure is made worse by poor organization and putting off doing things.

Groundwork

Time management requires a great deal of organization and good preparation. In other words you need to begin by investing time in laying the groundwork.

Laying the groundwork

You need some basic information about yourself and your routine before you can begin to reorganize your time. You need to balance your strengths, needs, priorities and goals with the demands on your time. You will need to look at:

- the way you work
- your routine
- your priorities
- your reasonable goals.

The way you work

Work through the questionnaire on the next page to get a sense of your organizational skills.

Look at your answers and then reflect on your strengths and needs as a time manager. You should aim to get the most out of your strengths without letting them disadvantage you. There might also be other qualities that you need to consider which have not been listed here, for example: Are you an innovator and a forward planner with lots of drive? Do you need people to bounce ideas off and get inspiration from or do you work more effectively alone?

Question	Answer	Advantage	Disadvantage
Are you the sort of person who plans ahead?	Yes	You can be well organized	You find it hard to be spontaneous
	No	You can be spontaneous	You might be poorly organized
Do you keep focusing on a goal until you have achieved it or are you easily distracted?	Focused		
	Easily distracted		
Are you punctual?	Yes		
	No		
Do you put things off?	No		
	Yes		
Do you obsess about a task?	No		
	Yes		
Do you make lists?	Yes		
	No		
Is your desk or work station cluttered or neat?	Neat		
	Cluttered		
Can you say 'No' to people?	Yes		
	No		
Do you like to follow tried and tested methods or come up with new ones?	New ones		
	Tried and tested		
Do you find it hard to delegate?	No		
	Yes		
Do you prefer to work alone?	No		
	Yes		

Make a list of your strengths and needs below.

Strengths	Needs
e.g. I plan ahead and am organized	I need to take the risk of being more spontaneous at times otherwise I may fail to come up with ideas that would help me be more efficient.
e.g. I can say 'No' and stick to my guns	I need to make sure that I'm always respectful of others, otherwise I might find that I create problems that I have to take extra time to deal with.
e.g. I'm innovative with lots of drive	I need to be aware of when I should rein in my creativity so that I don't waste time.

Your routine

You cannot manage your time effectively until you know how you are using it at the moment. The best way to find out is by keeping a record of how you use your time. By looking at your time diary, you will get an idea of where and when you use time productively, when you waste time and where you can make savings. Do not forget to log the time you spend on work when you are at home or the times when you slip into the office at weekends or in the evenings.

The same form of diary won't suit everyone, so you will need to tailor one to suit you. On the next two pages are three basic forms that you can use to start you off, with examples of each.

1 Listing your activities over set periods of time during the day. For example, you might break the day into 60-minute periods and at the end of each period record how you spent the preceding hour (see figure 1).

Figure 1

9.00am	Cleared away breakfast dishes, washed them and sat with a cup of coffee, making a shopping list. Began to read a new novel.
10.00am	Reading the novel instead of getting on with chores!
11.00am	Into the village to pick up the groceries and some wallpaper stripper.
12.00 noon	At home. Start to strip wallpaper in the children's room but change mind and begin to wash and rub down the paintwork instead. Run out of sandpaper so go into village to buy some more.
1.00pm	Run into Rose and have lunch in the café instead of going home.

2 Listing everything that you do, with a note of the start time and how long it takes (including interruptions and changes of task). A list of activities might include dealing with mail, answering the telephone, writing letters, etc. (see figure 2).

Figure 2

Task	Time began	Time finished	Time taken
Answer phone when I arrive in office	8.30	8.45	15 mins
Make coffee	8.45	8.50	5 mins
Talk with Susie about her day's work (interrupted by secretary: 5 mins)	8.50	9.30	40 mins
Meeting with line manager	9.30	11.00	90 mins

3 Listing your normal, daily tasks and logging the amount of time you spend on each (see figure 3).

Figure 3

My usual task	Total time taken on: Tuesday
1 Sorting bills	30 mins
2 Gardening	6 hours
3 Shopping	2 hours
4 Preparing meals	3 hours

Which type to use?

As a rough guide, the worse your problem with time management, the more information you need in order to regain control.

Studying your diary

Although this sort of record keeping might seem like hard work, you need only do it for a sample week or two. Once you have your log, stand back and study it. Answer the following questions based on what you've learnt from your diary. Then write down where you could make useful changes to your daily routine. Ask a friend to help if you find this difficult.

1 Do you have a healthy balance of work tasks? Or do you spend too much/too little time on certain tasks?

_____

_____

_____

_____

2 When do you carry out important tasks? Are you doing these when you might be less effective – when you are tired or rushed, for example?

_____

_____

_____

_____

3 Do you take breaks throughout the day? Do you take enough or too many?

_____

_____

_____

_____

4 Do you plan enough? Do you create time to do this? Could you deal with a crisis?

_____

_____

_____

_____

5 Do you review the work you've done? Do you create time to do this?

_____

_____

_____

_____

_____

Other areas for change or improvement.

_____

_____

_____

Working out your priorities

In order to allocate the time that you have available, you need to work out your priorities. If you don't do this you might find that you don't have enough time to get everything done. Or else you'll find you are overstretched. There may be certain work-related tasks that you can de-prioritize. For example, if you don't really think tidiness is very important to your job and feel that it is more important to develop your interests or career, you might usefully cut back on the time you spend keeping your office tidy.

So far, this section has focused on your work life. You also need to think about the best use of your time in an ideal world. This means thinking about all the areas of your life – career, health, family, money and so on – and deciding which are the most important. For example, you might rank your family above health and health above money and career. This will help you put your work life in the context of your 'real' life and make it easier to allocate the right amount of time to all the tasks you have to perform.

In the space below write down the important areas in your life. Then number them in order of most important (give this a 1) to least important.

My Priorities   **Ranking**

_____

_____

_____

_____

_____

_____

_____

_____

_____

_____

_____

Consider how much time you invest in each of your priorities. Are you balancing your time appropriately? If not, you may need to rethink and reorganize your life. Unless you spend time according to the priorities in your life you will be creating extra stress for yourself.

- Be clear about whether the priorities you have identified are really *your* priorities. Ask yourself questions like: 'Is this my responsibility?' 'Is this reasonable?' 'Do I want to do this?' Are you prioritizing shopping for the person next door because it matters to you or because you can't say no? Are you taking on extra teaching because it is a work priority for you or because it is a priority for your boss? If you have a job description, check whether your actual workload matches up with it.

- You may need to look at the chapter on assertiveness again (see page 29). This will help you limit your tasks to those which are unreasonable or which you really do choose to do.

Setting your goals

The last step is to determine your goals, so that you know what you are trying to achieve with your time. Read through the following tips, and then write down your short-, intermediate- and long-term goals in the space below.

Short-term goals are those which need to be tackled this week (e.g. getting the children to school on time).

Medium-term goals might be those you would want to achieve in the next month or so (e.g. making more time for regular exercise).

Long-term goals might cover six months or more (e.g. to get a new job or complete a training course).

Bear in mind what you have learnt about your strengths, needs, routine and priorities.

- When defining your goals, try to be as specific as possible. The more specific you are, the less easy it is to put them off or be distracted. Having clearly defined goals also makes it easier to appreciate when you have achieved them.

- Spell out who, what, when and how much. For example, the goal 'to be a better timekeeper' or 'to make time for myself' are too vague. More useful definitions would be:

  Goal: To arrive at the school, with the children, no later than 8.30 a.m. on quiet days and not later than 8.50 a.m. when I'm busy.

  Goal: To take a lunch break, starting between 12.30 and 1.00 p.m., which should last at least 30 minutes.

  These goals are clear, and also recognize the need for flexibility.

- Some goals can be achieved in a single step, but others need more planning. Revisit 'Grading tasks' on page 8 to see how to break down a big task into manageable steps. Again, this will reduce the temptation to delay putting things into action or give up.

- Be realistic and recognize your responsibilities and current circumstances, or you could set yourself unrealistic goals that simply cause you more anxiety.

- Learn to compromise and to rethink your goals regularly.

Short-term goals

_____

_____

_____

_____

_____

_____

_____

_____

_____

Medium-term goals

_____

_____

_____

_____

_____

_____

_____

_____

Long-term goals

_____

_____

_____

_____

_____

_____

_____

_____

Scheduling your time

Once you have laid the groundwork you can actually get down to the business of changing your daily, weekly and monthly schedules so that you manage your time more efficiently. Learn from your previous mistakes.

1 First, get yourself an organizer, such as a desk diary, a wall chart or a personal organizer – whatever suits you best.

2 Review your list of short-, medium- and long-term goals.

3 Make a review time for each list of goals so that you can check on your progress, update your values and priorities, and set more goals.

4 Every day, make time to go over and, if necessary, reorganize your schedule. Put this daily review time in your schedule.

5 Add time for a monthly review to your schedule. This may sound over-the-top, but if you don't include these review stages the system will break down.

6 Unforeseen crises or opportunities will arise, so don't be too rigid in your forward-planning.

Daily time management

The most important part of your daily time management routine should be drawing up a list of 'To-do' tasks, order them into four levels of urgency:

A Must do today

B Should do today

C Could put off

D Delegate (make someone else responsible for the task – see below).

Make drawing up this list a routine way to begin your day. It may take a little time but will save you a lot more time over the course of the day. Practise using the table on the next page. First, on a separate piece of paper, list all of the tasks you need to do tomorrow. Then write them in the table according to priority. Add more through the day as they occur to you. (There are additional blank tables at the back of this Part.)

A *Must* do today:

_____

B Should do today:

_____

C Could put off:

_____

D Delegate

Learning from difficulties

It is very likely, at first, that you won't manage to complete all your A and B tasks during the day. Use this as a learning experience – ask yourself why you didn't complete them, and how you could learn from this.

- Did the tasks prove too difficult or too time-consuming?
  If so, review Section 2, on problem-solving.

- Did you not meet your day's goals because you weren't able to say 'No' to interruptions?
  If so, you might need to be more assertive (see Section 3).

- Did you lose time because your work environment is badly organized and you can't get hold of things as you need them?

If so, use problem-solving to help you come up with good ideas for reorganizing your office.

- Were there simply too many things on your list?

Learn to delegate more (see below) or revise your expectations. If you have difficulty in delegating, or revising your expectations, identify the thoughts that get in the way and challenge them (see Part Two, page 51).

Delegating

A key tool in time management is delegation. You can't do everything yourself, and more importantly you shouldn't be expected to!

Many of your tasks could possibly be given to someone else. This might mean giving up some enjoyable jobs, but this will allow you overall more time to do the things that are really important to you.

It *isn't* faster to do everything yourself. Although training someone to 'do it properly' might take up time right now, it will pay off in the future.

How to delegate

1　Work out which tasks can be delegated.

2　Work out to whom you can give the task. The task must be suitable for the person who is to take it on. For example, it is no good asking your five-year-old son to wash and dress himself in his school uniform if he is not yet able to do up his buttons and tie laces.

3　Explain the task to the person very carefully – tell him or her exactly what is expected.

4　Train the person by monitoring and pacing them closely early on.

5　Then gradually reduce your supervision. Keep checking their progress.

6　Give the person the authority he or she needs to carry out the task, to go with the responsibility you are giving. If you give a worker or a family member a task you have to be able to stand back and risk that person making errors.

7　Allow time to review progress and performance with the person.

8　Remember that delegation is not an excuse for passing on all the boring or un-rewarding tasks. Others need fulfilment and challenge if you want them to cooperate and to develop in their own right.

Difficulties in using time management

'I haven't the time!'

This is the most common stumbling block for time management strategies. It's true that it does take time to get organized, but this is an investment for later. Time spent now will save you time and anxiety in the long run, and you will be taking charge of your life instead of just reacting to events.

'It's no good: it doesn't work for me'

This is most likely to reflect poor planning and not giving enough time to the task of analysis and reorganization. Don't compromise by being half-hearted. You also need to allow time for your new system to be accepted by those around you.

'I can't delegate'

Among the most common objections to delegating are: 'It's easier/faster to do it myself'; 'If you want a good job doing, do it yourself'; 'I haven't the time to show her how to do it'; 'He couldn't manage it'; 'She wouldn't do it properly'; 'At the end of the day, I'm responsible'. Write down these statements and then think of ways in which you can challenge them (see Part Two, page 51 on challenging unhelpful thoughts).

Summary

1 For good personal organization you need to:
   know your strengths and needs
   know your routine
   know your priorities
   know how to set reasonable goals.

2 In order to manage time effectively, you need to come up with a workable system for yourself which meets *your* needs and which you review and revise regularly.

3 Learn to delegate, but give the person authority and training in the task.

SECTION 5: Getting a Better Night's Sleep

As many as one in five people complain of difficulty in dropping off to sleep, of waking too frequently during the night or of waking too early in the morning. It is quite normal to have an interrupted night's sleep. Difficulty in sleeping tends only becomes a problem when it worries you. You can then fall into in a vicious cycle where anxiety stops you getting to sleep, which then causes you more anxiety. In fact worrying about not sleeping can be more uncomfortable and tiring than the lack of sleep itself.

You can improve your sleep pattern by learning more about sleep and by changing your behaviour and improving the environment in which you sleep. This section will cover:

- Some important but less well-known facts about sleep that may reassure you about your own sleep patterns

- Why sleeping pills can be a problem rather than a solution

- How you can get to know your own sleep patterns so that you know where to make improvements

- How to ensure healthy sleep habits and how to create the best environment for sleep

- Sleep problems other than difficulty in falling asleep/early waking, and whether you should worry about them

What is a normal sleep pattern?

You may be worrying about sleep patterns that are perfectly normal.

- There is no such thing as the ideal length of sleep: some people need ten hours and some three. Your best indicator of need is how you feel after different periods of sleep.

- As you get older, you need less sleep.

- Everyone has 'broken' sleep. It's normal to wake several times during the night and simply go back to sleep, often without registering the waking. It is only when you worry about waking that you will notice it, and then this worrying can keep you awake.

- It is not harmful to lose a few 'good' nights' sleep. Everyone has the odd period of poor sleep, especially when under stress. The only ill effect of this is that you will feel tired during the day and might find yourself more irritable or less able to cope with things. Once your sleep pattern is restored, you will feel fine again.

- Sleep is affected by many things – stress, mood, exercise, food, medicines, alcohol. By changing some of these things, you can take control of your sleeping pattern without having to use sleeping pills.

Why avoid sleeping pills?

The simple answer to this question is that sleeping tablets are rarely helpful in the long term and are often addictive. An occasional sleeping pill, taken on your doctor's advice, might be useful in a crisis, for example, but your body can begin to rely on them and it can then become difficult to sleep without medication. When you stop taking sleeping tablets, you can find that your sleep pattern is worse than ever and that you are tempted to go back on the tablets. This can be the beginning of a cycle of poor sleep and dependency on drugs. Fortunately, you can often deal with sleep problems without having to take sleeping pills, simply by changing your behaviour.

Know your own sleep patterns

First, keep a sleep diary to find out more about your sleep patterns. Complete this in the morning – do not interrupt your sleep by trying to fill it in during the night. It should include the following columns:

- The date and any event which might affect your sleep: for example, what food you ate before going to bed, what level of stress you were under, what exercise you took, etc.

- How many hours of sleep you had.

- How many times you remember waking during the night.

- What you did when you could not sleep: for example, made a cup of tea, read, looked at the ceiling.

- Whether or not this helped.

- How alert or awake you felt the next day. You could rate yourself on a 10-point scale where 1 means 'Felt as dull and sleepy as I can imagine', and 10 means 'Felt fully alert and awake.'

- How well you carried out your work the next day, again using a 10-point scale.

On the next page you will find a sleep diary. Fill in the diary for a week or two (there are additional blank diary sheets at the back of this Part).

Do you have a problem?

After you have kept the diary for at least a week, you can assess whether you have a sleeping problem at all. If you are feeling reasonably alert and working reasonably well on your usual number of hours' sleep, then you don't have a problem. If you are feeling tired and your work is suffering, use your diary to help you complete the next part.

1 Study your sleep diary: is poor sleep linked with life stresses and therefore likely to improve as the stress eases? In the space below write down some of the stressful events which you know will pass in time.
Stresses that will pass

_____

_____

_____

_____

2 Are there particular things you do before bed which seem to cause a poor night's sleep? For example, eating certain foods or drinking. Write them in the space below.
Things that cause a bad night's sleep

_____

_____

_____

_____

Sleep diary

Date	Significant events before bed	Number of hours of sleep	Number of times I woke during night	What I did when I couldn't sleep	Did this help (yes or no)	How alert I felt the next day (rank out of 10)	How well I performed the next day (rank out of 10)

3 Are there things you do before bed which seem to help you get a good night's sleep? For example, listening to relaxing music. Write them in the space below.
Things that help me sleep well

_____

_____

_____

4 If you woke during the night, what didn't help you go back to sleep? Write them in the space below.
Things that didn't help me get back to sleep

_____

_____

_____

5 What did help you to go back to sleep? Write them in the space below.
Things that helped me get back to sleep

_____

_____

_____

You can now use this knowledge to reassure yourself if you realize that stress-related sleep problems will pass, you can maximize those things that are conducive to a good night's sleep or getting back to sleep and you can minimize those things that either impair your sleep or do not help you get back to sleep.

Suggestions for a better night's sleep

- Try to relax: remember that no one has unbroken sleep and everyone has the odd period of poor sleep. If you don't worry, you will sleep better. Make time to relax an hour or two before you go to bed. For example, take a gentle stroll or a warm bath, or sit and listen to soothing music. Use relaxation exercises and distraction exercises (see Sections 4 and 5 in Part Two) to keep your tension at a minimum when you are in bed.

- Keep your daily stress low by making sure that you are not overworking and that you are dealing with problems as they arise and not taking them to bed with you as worrying thoughts. You might consider getting the support of friends or a professional counsellor if you find it too difficult to deal with work stress or emotional problems by yourself.

- Take exercise in the day.

- Avoid caffeine (in chocolate, tea, coffee, cocoa and cola). Try having a warm milky drink before bed. Cut down on alcohol and nicotine at night: although these are sedative in small doses, alcohol becomes a stimulant as it is broken down and nicotine becomes a stimulant in larger doses. Avoid spicy food or a heavy meal in the evening, but do not go to bed hungry as this will keep you awake. Try having a light snack.

- Make sure that your bedroom is quiet and that your bed is comfortable, and empty your bladder before you try to go to sleep.

- Go to bed only when you are sleepy, and use your bed only for sleeping – not eating or reading or watching the television – at least until you have re-established a good sleep pattern. It is important that your bed becomes associated with sleep and not waking activities.

- If you have not fallen asleep after fifteen to twenty minutes, or if you wake and do not go back to sleep, get out of bed and do something else until you feel sleepy. Do something simple and not too energetic, like light housework or reading, then try to sleep again. Keep repeating this until you do fall asleep rather than lie in bed tossing and turning, as that will tend to increase your agitation.

- Set an alarm so that you wake at a regular time each day: you will find that you sleep better if you have a regular routine. Get up when your alarm goes off and don't be tempted to catch up on your sleep during the day or through 'sleep binges' at the weekends. For the time being, you are trying to establish a good sleep pattern.

- If you follow these suggestions, and practise relaxation, you should have less difficulty in sleeping. If the problem does persist, particularly early morning wakening, then see your doctor for further advice.

Read how Allan dealt with his sleep problems to give you ideas about lifestyle changes you could make.

CASE STUDY: Allan

'I thought that I was simply a light sleeper, that I could never expect to sleep as well as my wife. Then we took our dream holiday – a real get-away-from-it-all vacation. We swam, we walked, we forgot work and I slept like a log.

'Once we returned home, my sleep again became broken and I felt tired the next day. So we sat down and worked out how I could get a good night's sleep again. We realized that the things that had made a difference for me were: I did not worry about the business; I exercised and relaxed every day; and we ate and drank healthily. Now that I knew that it was possible for me to sleep well, I was very motivated to try to restore my holiday sleep pattern.

'I gave up coffee and alcohol in the evenings: I left work in the very early evening so that we had time to do something relaxing each night – this might be going to the theatre, or hiring a video or playing a game of squash. On those evenings when I could not avoid working late, I made sure that I took a relaxing bath with a good book before going to bed – this way I could clear my mind of worries. I began to sleep better within days. I wish I'd done it sooner.'

Other sleep problems

From time to time, you might worry about other sleep-related experiences which are not harmful. For example:

Sleep paralysis During some parts of sleep, our bodies are 'paralysed' so that we do not act out our dreams. Sometimes, on drowsing or waking, we can experience a very temporary episode of wakefulness without the ability to move. This can be frightening but it will last only a second or so.

Sensory shocks These are harmless bodily sensations in the form of jerks or the sensation of falling which might be vivid enough to wake the sleeper.

Hallucinations These can occur when a person is in a state of half-sleep or dozing or waking. They are normal and fleeting but can be vivid enough to be alarming.

None of these experiences is harmful and accepting them is the best way of dealing with them. However, *sleepwalking* can be dangerous and it is advisable to discuss this with a general practitioner or a specialist.

Difficulties in using sleep management

'I still have the odd night of poor sleep'

You can expect this to continue. We all have the occasional night when we don't sleep well and this should not seriously affect our work or the quality of our lives. It is a good idea to note when you have a poor night's sleep so that you can learn what affects your sleep pattern.

'I still can't sleep for more than a few hours'

Study your sleep diary – do you function well on a few hours' sleep? If so, don't worry, just make the most of it. If not, take another look at your sleep habits: perhaps you need to use more relaxation exercises, cut down even more on stimulants or work on distraction techniques to tackle worrying thoughts (see Part Two).

'I would sleep well if only my partner didn't keep waking me'

If your partner wakes you because he or she is a poor sleeper, get him or her to read this chapter. If your partner wakes you because of his or her disturbing behaviour (sleepwalking, snoring, sensory shock, etc.), you might have to consider sleeping separately if you want a good night's sleep. If your partner sleepwalks or snores badly, you should encourage him or her to see a doctor.

Summary

1 Worry, more than anything, will interrupt your sleep.

2 Familiarize yourself with facts about sleep so that you do not worry unnecessarily.

3 Prepare yourself before going go bed: watch what you eat and drink, relax, don't lie awake in bed and don't 'catnap' during the day.

SECTION 6: Coping in the Long Term

This final section will explain how you can maintain your achievements so that worry, fear and anxiety are not a problem in the future. The best way to do this is to keep practising your new skills, so that they become easier to use and more effective. You can further 'stress-proof' your life by using the skills you have learned to help you anticipate and overcome problems and setbacks in the future. This section looks at ways you can do this through:

- Blueprinting

- Learning from setbacks

- Making coping strategies part of your lifestyle

- Preparing for anxiety or panic attacks

Blueprinting

This is also known as **troubleshooting**. You need to set aside some time for thinking about future challenges and when stress might be likely to affect you. You might list challenges like: 'Giving a presentation to my co-workers' or 'Taking this faulty television back to the shop'. Write down your challenges for the near future in the space below.

_____

_____

_____

_____

_____

_____

_____

_____

Planning to meet challenges

Once you have predicted those situations which will be stressful for you, use what you have learned in this Part to plan how you will deal with each challenge. Think how you might prepare yourself by relaxing and by rehearsing before you are in the situation, and then plan how you will deal with the stress when you face it. Which of your coping techniques will help you? Consider how you will deal with the situation if everything does not go according to plan; have a back-up scheme.

If you anticipate difficult times and predict your needs during such periods, you can organize your life to minimize your distress and the risk of losing confidence. For example, if you know that Christmas pressures always cause stress and leave you feeling miserable, panicky and likely to turn to chocolate and alcohol for comfort, you could reorganize your Christmas activities to limit your stress. You might plan a holiday; you could make sure that you did not have easy access to alcohol and chocolate; you could schedule time to yourself, you could practise saying 'No'. Look at your list and work out some plans for coping; make a note of these in the space below.

Challenge   **Plan for coping**

_____

_____

_____

_____

_____

_____

_____

_____

_____

_____

_____

Coping with an anxiety attack or a panic attack

It is always easier to cope with anxiety in its early stages, and this is why it is helpful to recognize the onset of tension, and to use this as your cue for putting coping techniques into action. However, there may be times when you miss the early signs and you become highly anxious or panicky. At this point it is hard to think clearly and act rationally, so it is important to have learnt what to do if you get extremely anxious or have a panic attack. If you are well prepared, you will be able to manage your feelings.

Remember, *your feelings are normal and harmless.*

Use *controlled breathing* to ease your discomfort and give you enough relief for you to be able to think more clearly .

Accept what is happening to you. If you wait, the fear will pass; if you run away, it will be more difficult to cope with the situation in the future.

Control frightening thoughts. Try to use distraction or to think of the situation in a more balanced or logical way.

As soon as you are able, *make a plan* to ease the situation. You could rest until you feel calmer or get the help of a friend, for example. Whatever you decide, try to carry it out in a relaxed way.

Learning from setbacks

Even the best-laid plans can come unstuck, and sometimes you will feel that you have let yourself down. This is when you are most vulnerable to a relapse back to your old anxieties and maintaining cycles. If you view a setback or a disappointment as a failure you will feel demoralized and the confidence you have been building over the course of this programme will be sapped.

If, however, you use a setback as an opportunity to learn more about your strengths and needs, you can turn a disappointment to your advantage. Each setback tells you something about yourself and how a particular situation makes you vulnerable. You can use this information to increase your chances of overcoming or defusing anxiety in the future. The case study on the next page shows an example.

CASE STUDY: Gina

When Gina took her faulty iron back to the shop to complain, things did not go according to plan. She had rehearsed entering the shop and speaking calmly but firmly to the shop assistant, but in fact the streets were crowded and the buses were running late, so she arrived hot and flustered. When she got there, there was a different assistant from usual, and she felt so anxious that she fled without speaking to him. When she got home she felt terrible, but rather than accept defeat she reviewed the situation and made an improved plan. Next time she would wait for a cooler day, go at a less busy time, mentally rehearse for dealing with any assistant, and, as a back-up plan, arrange to meet a friend for coffee around the corner so that she could return with support if necessary.

When confronting your own setbacks, remember that:

- Slips and setbacks will happen. A *lapse* does not necessarily mean *collapse*.

- Setbacks are opportunities to improve your performance next time.

Making coping strategies part of your lifestyle

For further 'stress-proofing', try to integrate the various strategies you have learned into your day-to-day routines.

- Build a 'relaxation slot' into your daily routine. This might only take a few minutes but it will be a valuable use of your time. Try to develop the habit of relaxing. See Part Two, Section 4.

- Do as many pleasurable things as possible: if your pleasurable activities release tension too, so much the better. You might try physical exercise and yoga.

- Tackle stress early – don't let it build up. If something is worrying you, seek advice from friends or professionals. Find out now where you might seek help – have a list of useful telephone numbers, including friends and organizations such as the Samaritans.

- Get organized at home and at work. If you need professional help, find a time-management course in your area. See Section 4.

- Assert yourself at home and at work. Avoid the unnecessary stress of being a doormat or being exploited. Look out for local assertiveness training classes or get a specialist book on assertiveness out of the library. See Section 3.

- Avoid getting overtired or taking on too much work. Recognize when you have reached your limit and stop. Take a break and try to do something relaxing and/or pleasurable.

- Don't avoid what you fear. If you find something is becoming difficult for you to face up to, don't back away – if you do, that situation will only grow more frightening. Instead, set yourself a series of small and safe steps to help you meet the challenge. See Section 1.

- Remember to recognize your achievements and to praise yourself. Never downgrade yourself and don't dwell on past difficulties. Give yourself credit for what you do achieve, and look and plan ahead.

Summary

1   Coping in the long term requires regular practice of all that you have learnt.

2   Establish blueprints to cope with upcoming challenges.

3   Know how to manage an anxiety or panic attack.

4   Learn from setbacks.

5   Incorporate coping strategies into your daily routine: change your lifestyle to minimize stress.

Extra Charts and Worksheets

Diary

Date	Task	Anxiety rating (1–10)	Other relevant information

Diary

Date	Task	Anxiety rating (1–10)	Other relevant information

Diary

Date	Task	Anxiety rating (1–10)	Other relevant information

Diary

Date	Task	Anxiety rating (1–10)	Other relevant information

Daily time management

A *Must* do today:

B Should do today:

C Could put off:

D Delegate

Daily time management

A *Must* do today:

_____

B Should do today:

_____

C Could put off:

_____

D Delegate

Daily time management

A *Must* do today:

B Should do today:

C Could put off:

D Delegate

Daily time management

A *Must* do today:

_____

B Should do today:

_____

C Could put off:

_____

D Delegate

Sleep diary

Date	Significant events before bed	Number of hours of sleep	Number of times I woke during night	What I did when I couldn't sleep	Did this help (yes or no)	How alert I felt the next day (rank out of 10)	How well I performed the next day (rank out of 10)

Sleep diary

Date	Significant events before bed	Number of hours of sleep	Number of times I woke during night	What I did when I couldn't sleep	Did this help (yes or no)	How alert I felt the next day (rank out of 10)	How well I performed the next day (rank out of 10)

Sleep diary

Date	Significant events before bed	Number of hours of sleep	Number of times I woke during night	What I did when I couldn't sleep	Did this help (yes or no)	How alert I felt the next day (rank out of 10)	How well I performed the next day (rank out of 10)

Sleep diary

Date	Significant events before bed	Number of hours of sleep	Number of times I woke during night	What I did when I couldn't sleep	Did this help (yes or no)	How alert I felt the next day (rank out of 10)	How well I performed the next day (rank out of 10)

Sleep diary

Date	Significant events before bed	Number of hours of sleep	Number of times I woke during night	What I did when I couldn't sleep	Did this help (yes or no)	How alert I felt the next day (rank out of 10)	How well I performed the next day (rank out of 10)

Writing your own script

The problem:

_____

_____

_____

Your explanation:

_____

_____

_____

_____

Your feelings:

_____

_____

_____

Your needs:

_____

_____

_____

The consequences:

_____

_____

_____

Writing your own script

The problem:

_____

_____

_____

Your explanation:

_____

_____

_____

Your feelings:

_____

_____

_____

Your needs:

_____

_____

_____

The consequences:

_____

_____

_____

Writing your own script

The problem:

_____

_____

_____

Your explanation:

_____

_____

_____

_____

Your feelings:

_____

_____

_____

Your needs:

_____

_____

_____

The consequences:

_____

_____

_____

Writing your own script

The problem:

_____

_____

_____

Your explanation:

_____

_____

_____

_____

Your feelings:

_____

_____

_____

Your needs:

_____

_____

_____

The consequences:

_____

_____

_____

Order further books in the Overcoming series

No. of copies	Title	Price	Total
	Overcoming Anxiety Self-Help Course	£21.00	
	Overcoming Low Self-Esteem Self-Help Course	£21.00	
	Overcoming Bulimia Nervosa and Binge-Eating Self-Help Course	£21.00	
	Overcoming Anger and Irritability	£9.99	
	Overcoming Anorexia Nervosa	£9.99	
	Overcoming Anxiety	£9.99	
	Bulimia Nervosa and Binge-Eating	£9.99	
	Overcoming Childhood Trauma	£9.99	
	Overcoming Chronic Fatigue	£9.99	
	Overcoming Chronic Pain	£9.99	
	Overcoming Compulsive Gambling	£9.99	
	Overcoming Depression	£9.99	
	Overcoming Insomnia and Sleep Problems	£9.99	
	Overcoming Low Self-Esteem	£9.99	
	Overcoming Mood Swings	£9.99	
	Overcoming Obsessive Compulsive Disorder	£9.99	
	Overcoming Panic	£9.99	
	Overcoming Relationship Problems	£9.99	
	Overcoming Sexual Problems	£9.99	
	Overcoming Social Anxiety and Shyness	£9.99	
	Overcoming Traumatic Stress	£9.99	
	Overcoming Weight Problems	£9.99	
	Overcoming Your Smoking Habit	£9.99	
	P & P free	Grand TOTAL £	

Name: _____

Delivery Address: _____

_____

_____

Postcode: _____

Daytime Tel. No.: _____

Email: _____

How to pay:

1. **By telephone**: call the TBS order line on 01206 522 800 and quote SHBK1. Phone lines are open between Monday – Friday, 8.30am – 5.30pm.

2. **By post**: send a cheque for the full amount payable to TBS Ltd. and send form to:

Freepost RLUL-SJGC-SGKJ,
Cash Sales/Direct Mail Dept.,
The Book Service,
Colchester Road, Frating,
Colchester CO7 7DW